The Roger Jones Hymn Collection

New tunes to well-loved words

Foreword by Nigel Swinford

*To Annie - a friend, colleague and
encourager in the work of the Lord*

Kevin
Mayhew

We hope you enjoy the music in this book.
Further copies of this and our many other books are
available from your local music shop or Christian bookshop.

In case of difficulty, please contact the publisher direct by writing to:

The Sales Department
KEVIN MAYHEW LTD
Buxhall
Stowmarket
Suffolk IP14 3BW

Phone 01449 737978
Fax 01449 737834
E-mail info@kevinmayhewltd.com

Please ask for our complete catalogue of outstanding Church Music.

First published in Great Britain in 1999 by Kevin Mayhew Ltd.

ISBN 1 84003 385 1
ISMN M 57004 553 2
Catalogue No: 1450144

0 1 2 3 4 5 6 7 8 9

Cover design by Jonathan Stroulger.

Music Editor/Setter: Donald Thomson
Proof-reader: Kate Gallaher

Please note, all Christian Music Ministries © songs are administered by:
Sovereign Music UK, PO Box 356, Leighton Buzzard, Beds., LU7 8WP

Printed and bound in Great Britain

Contents

Roger Jones is Britain's foremost composer of Christian musicals and cantatas. He has also written a number of collections of Psalms, Hymns and Spiritual Songs (Eph. 5:18; Col. 3:16). This is a collection of Roger Jones' new tunes to well-loved texts. Many come from the musicals; some have been written independently. Roger feels that giving traditional hymn words new musical contours can often help people appreciate afresh the truths contained in our rich heritage of hymns.

Ann Routley, the arranger of many of these hymns, has worked alongside Roger Jones at Christian Music Ministries since September 1994. A music graduate with a wide experience in playing viola and keyboards, and singing in choirs, small groups and broadcasts, Ann has in recent years with CMM been developing skills in orchestration and writing arrangements for groups in order to encourage musicians with a range of abilities.

Foreword

Roger Jones' love and respect for the great tradition of English language hymnody is eloquently expressed in this delightful collection of new tunes. I completely share his enthusiasm and am in favour of anything that keeps these priceless items of heritage in current usage.

The great value of these hymns is the way in which they encapsulate the key points of Christian theology so faithfully and so winningly. Whilst the modern spiritual song tends to be more subjective in outlook, these masterpieces of communication show us the big picture, God's great plan of salvation for mankind through his Son, Jesus. They beckon us onwards, upwards, inviting us to be part of something so much greater than ourselves and our immediate circumstances. Thank you, Roger, for writing these melodies, and Ann Routley, for devising such clear and unfussy accompaniments. I suggest that they may turn out to be an invaluable means of introducing the next generation to the treasure-store of Christian thought contained in the words of our great hymns.

NIGEL SWINFORD

Note about using the backing tracks

The great advantage of singing to backing tracks is that it provides accompaniment and instruments that may not be available in the local situation. Singers also find it a great thrill to be accompanied by a larger instrumental ensemble. The attached CD (inside the back cover) contains the accompaniment for 21 of the hymns in this book. They are actually taken from the associated album, *Roger Jones Hymn Collection - Volume One*, which is published by Kevin Mayhew Ltd.

Using backing tracks does not do away with the need to rehearse. Leaders, vocalists or choirs should become very familiar with speed, introductions, modulations, instrumental links and codas before using the tracks in worship. There must also be adequate sound reproduction equipment, appropriate to the size and acoustics of the room.

1 All people that on earth do dwell

Text: William Kethe (d.1594) from 'Day's Psalter' (1560) alt.
Music: Roger Jones arr. Ann Routley from 'Saints Alive'

SAINTS ALIVE   88 88 (LM)

Fanfare: Maestoso (♩ = 110)

1. All people that on earth do dwell, sing to the Lord with cheerful voice; him serve with mirth, his praise forth tell; come ye before him and rejoice.

2. O enter then his gates with praise,
   approach with joy his courts unto;
   praise, laud and bless his name always,
   for it is seemly so to do.
   For why, the Lord our God is good:
   his mercy is for ever sure;
   his truth at all times firmly stood,
   and shall from age to age endure.

3. Praise God from whom all blessings flow,
   praise him all creatures here below,
   praise him above ye heav'nly host,
   praise Father, Son and Holy Ghost!
   Praise God from whom all blessings flow,
   praise him all creatures here below,
   praise him above ye heavn'ly host,
   praise Father, Son and Holy Ghost!

2 And can it be?

Words: Charles Wesley (1707-1788)
Music: Roger Jones from 'Pharisee'

NICODEMUS 88 88 88 extended

The last two lines of each verse should be sung twice.

2. 'Tis myst'ry all! Th' Immortal dies:
   who can explore his strange design?
   In vain the first-born seraph tries
   to sound the depths of love divine!
   'Tis mercy all! Let earth adore,
   let angel minds inquire no more.

3. He left his Father's throne above,
   so free, so infinite his grace;
   emptied himself of all but love,
   and bled for Adam's helpless race;
   'tis mercy all, immense and free;
   for, O my God, it found out me.

4. Long my imprisoned spirit lay
   fast bound in sin and nature's night;
   thine eye diffused a quickening ray,
   I woke, the dungeon flamed with light;
   my chains fell off, my heart was free;
   I rose, went forth, and followed thee.

5. No condemnation now I dread;
   Jesus, and all in him, is mine!
   Alive in him, my living Head,
   and clothed in righteousness divine,
   bold I approach the eternal throne,
   and claim the crown, through Christ my own.

3 Angel-voices ever singing

Words: Francis Pott (1832-1909)
Music: Roger Jones arr. Ann Routley from 'Angel Voices'

THRONE OF LIGHT   85 85 843

and con - fess thee Lord of might.

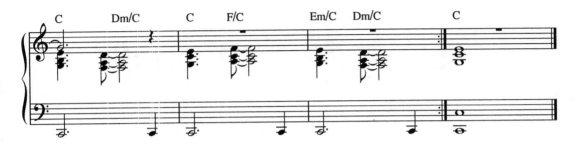

2. Thou who art beyond the farthest
   mortal eye can scan,
   can it be that thou regardest
   songs of sinful man?
   Can we know that thou art near us
   and wilt hear us? Yes, we can!

3. Yes, we know that thou rejoicest
   o'er each work of thine;
   thou didst ears and hands and voices
   for thy praise design;
   craftsman's art and music's measure
   for thy pleasure all combine.

4. In thy house, great God, we offer
   of thine own to thee;
   and for thine acceptance proffer
   all unworthily,
   hearts and minds and hands and voices
   in our choicest psalmody.

5. Honour, glory, might and merit,
   thine shall ever be,
   Father, Son and Holy Spirit,
   blessed Trinity.
   Of the best that thou hast given
   earth and heaven render thee.

4 Break thou the bread of life

Words: Mary Lathbury and A. Groves
Music: Roger Jones arr. Ann Routley from 'Greater Than Gold'

2. Thou art the bread of life,
O Lord, to me,
thy holy word the truth
that saveth me.
Give me to eat and live
with thee above;
teach me to love thy truth,
for thou art love.

3. O send thy Spirit, Lord,
now unto me,
that he may touch my eyes
and make me see.
Show me the truth concealed
within thy word;
that in thy book revealed,
I see thee, Lord.

5 Breathe on me, Breath of God

Words: Edwin Hatch (1835-1889)
Music: Roger Jones arr. Ann Routley from 'Saints Alive'

do and to en - dure.

2. Breathe on me, Breath of God,
   fulfil my heart's desire,
   until this earthly part of me
   glows with thy heavenly fire.
   Breathe on me, Breath of God,
   so shall I never die,
   but live with thee the perfect life
   of thine eternity.

Optional harmony parts for SAT

Breathe on me, Breath of God, fill me with life a - new,

that I may love what thou dost love and do what thou wouldst do.

Breathe on me, Breath of God, un - til my heart is pure:

un - til with thee I will one will to do and to en - dure.

6 Christ is alive!

Words: Christopher Ellis (b.1949)
Music: Roger Jones from 'Precious and Honoured'

ELLIS 86 96
With strength ($\downarrow$ = 125)

1. Christ is a-live and all   is changed: the cross and tomb are bare!
3. Christ is a-live, he leaves   the tomb,   the grave of our des-pair.

A new cre-a-tion bursts in-to life   and hope   be-gins to dare.
The place of death be-comes   a womb: new life   for all to share!

2. Christ is a-live and all   is   clear   that was mis-un-der-stood.
4. Christ is a-live, our lov-er   comes   and seeks our hearts to woo.

The pain and death   are ful-ly re-deemed,   the   world
The claims of love   are not   a mis-take: God's   love

7 Dear Lord and Father of mankind

Words: John Greenleaf Whittier (1807-1882)
Music: Roger Jones arr. Anne Routley from 'Mary Magdalene'

2. In simple trust like theirs who heard,
   beside the Syrian sea,
   the gracious calling of the Lord,
   let us, like them, without a word,
   rise up and follow thee.

3. O Sabbath rest by Galilee!
   O calm of hills above,
   where Jesus knelt to share with thee
   the silence of eternity,
   interpreted by love!

4. With that deep hush subduing all,
   our words and works that drown,
   the tender whisper of thy call,
   as noiseless let thy blessing fall,
   as fell thy manna down.

5. Drop thy still dews of quietness,
   till all our strivings cease;
   take from our souls the strain and stress,
   and let our ordered lives confess
   the beauty of thy peace.

6. Breathe through the heats of our desire
   thy coolness and thy balm;
   let sense be dumb, let flesh retire;
   speak through the earthquake, wind and fire,
   O still small voice of calm!

8 For the beauty of the earth

Words: Folliot Sandford Pierpoint (1835-1917)
Music: Roger Jones from 'Ways to Praise'

SACRIFICE OF PRAISE   77 77 77
Moderato con moto

2. For the beauty of each hour
   of the day and of the night,
   hill and vale and tree and flower,
   sun and moon and stars of light:

3. For the joy of ear and eye,
   for the heart and brain's delight,
   for the mystic harmony
   linking sense to sound and sight:

4. For the joy of human love,
   brother, sister, parent, child,
   friends on earth, and friends above,
   for all gentle thoughts and mild:

5. For each perfect gift of thine,
   to our race so freely given,
   graces, human and divine,
   flowers of earth and buds of heaven:

9 God of mercy, God of grace

Words: Henry Francis Lyte (1793-1847) from Psalm 67
Music: Roger Jones arr. Ann Routley from 'Ways to Praise'

GOD OF MERCY   77 77 77

Gently (♩ = 85)

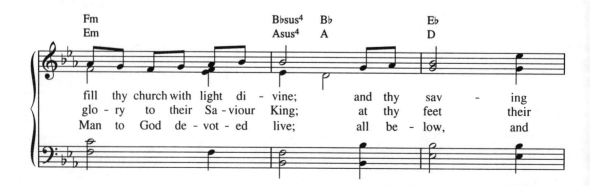

10 Go forth and tell!

Words: James Seddon (1915-1983)
Music: Roger Jones

2. Go forth and tell! God's love embraces all;
   he will in grace respond to all who call:
   how shall they call if they have never heard
   the gracious invitation of his word?

3. Go forth and tell! where still the darkness lies;
   in wealth or want, the sinner surely dies:
   give us, O Lord, concern of heart and mind,
   a love like yours, which cares for all mankind.

4. Go forth and tell! The doors are open wide:
   share God's good gifts – let no one be denied;
   live out your life as Christ your Lord shall choose,
   your ransomed powers for his sole glory use.

5. Go forth and tell! O church of God, arise!
   Go in the strength which Christ your Lord supplies;
   Go till all nations his great name adore
   and serve him, Lord and King for evermore.

11 Guide me, O my great Redeemer

Words: William Williams (1717-1791) and others
Music: Roger Jones arr. Ann Routley from 'From Pharaoh to Freedom'

WARD END   87 87 47 extended

Andante con moto ($\downarrow$ = c.64)

2. Open now the crystal fountain,
   where the healing waters flow;
   let the fiery cloudy pillar
   lead me all my journey through:
   strong deliverer, strong deliverer,
   ever be my strength and shield;
   strong deliverer, strong deliverer,
   ever be my strength and shield.

3. When I tread the verge of Jordan,
   bid my anxious fears subside;
   death of death, and hell's destruction,
   land me safe on Canaan's side:
   songs of praises, songs of praises,
   all my joy shall ever be;
   songs of praises, songs of praises,
   all my joy shall ever be.

12 Holy, holy, holy!

Words: Reginald Heber (1783-1826)
Music: Roger Jones arr. Ann Routley from 'Angel Voices'

BLESSED TRINITY   11 12 12 10
Andante con moto (♩ = 90)

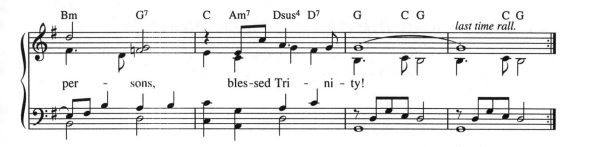

per - sons,   bles-sed Tri - ni - ty!

2. Holy, holy, holy!
   all the saints adore thee,
   casting down their golden crowns
   around the glassy sea;
   cherubim and seraphim
   falling down before thee,
   who were, and are,
   and evermore shall be.

3. Holy, holy, holy!
   though the darkness hide thee,
   though the eye of sinful man
   thy glory may not see,
   only thou art holy,
   there is none beside thee,
   perfect in power,
   in love, and purity.

4. Holy, holy, holy!
   Lord God almighty!
   All thy works shall praise thy name,
   in earth, and sky, and sea;
   holy, holy, holy!
   merciful and mighty!
   God in three persons,
   blessed Trinity!

13 How sweet the name of Jesus sounds

Words: John Henry Newton (1725-1807)
Music: Roger Jones arr. Ann Routley from 'Stargazers'

HOW SWEET   86 86   (CM)
With simplicity (♩ = 90)

How sweet the name of Je - sus sounds

in a be - liev - er's ear! It

soothes our sor - rows, heals our wounds,

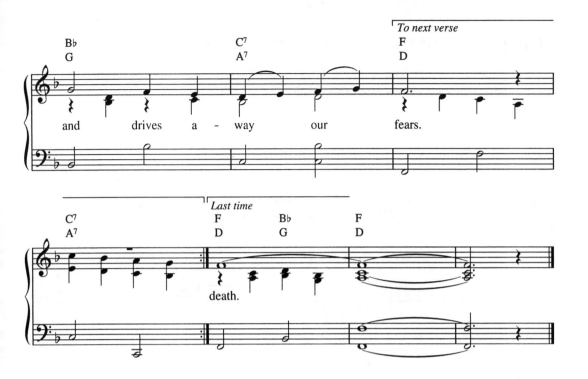

To next verse

and drives a - way our fears.

Last time

death.

2. It makes the wounded spirit whole,
   and calms the troubled breast;
   'tis manna to the hungry soul,
   and to the weary, rest.

3. Dear name! the rock on which I build,
   my shield and hiding-place,
   my never-failing treasury filled
   with boundless stores of grace.

4. Jesus! my shepherd, Saviour, friend,
   my prophet, priest, and king,
   my Lord, my life, my way, my end,
   accept the praise I bring.

5. Weak is the effort of my heart,
   and cold my warmest thought;
   but when I see thee as thou art,
   I'll praise thee as I ought.

6. Till then I would thy love proclaim
   with every fleeting breath;
   and may the music of thy name
   refresh my soul in death.

14 I am trusting thee, Lord Jesus

Words: Frances Ridley Havergal (1836-1879)
Music: Roger Jones arr. Ann Routley from 'Precious and Honoured'

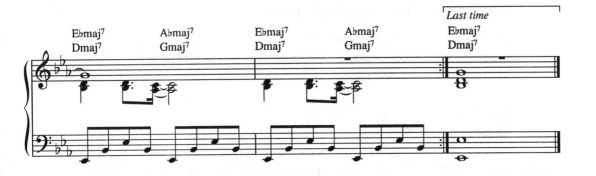

3. I am trusting thee for cleansing
   in the crimson flood;
   trusting thee to make me holy
   by thy blood.

4. I am trusting thee to guide me;
   thou alone shalt lead,
   every day and hour supplying
   all my need, all my need.

5. I am trusting thee for power,
   thine can never fail;
   words which thou thyself shalt give me
   must prevail.

6. I am trusting thee, Lord Jesus;
   never let me fall;
   I am trusting thee for ever,
   and for all, and for all.

15 I heard the voice of Jesus say

Words: Horatius Bonar (1808-1889)
Music: Roger Jones arr. Ann Routley from 'Mary Magdalene'

VOICE OF JESUS   86 86 D (DCM)
Steady rock (♩ = 65)

1. I heard the voice of Je - sus say, 'Come un - to me and rest; lay down, O wea - ry one, lay down your head up - on my breast!' I came to Je - sus as I was, wea - ry and worn and sad;

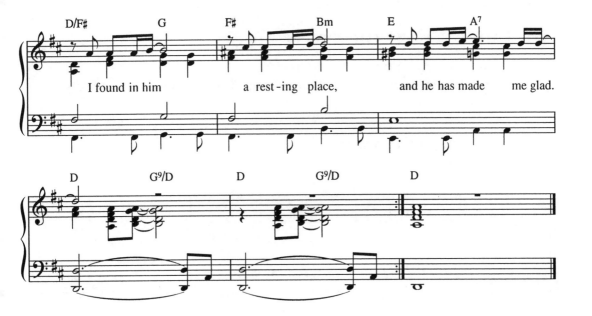

I found in him   a rest-ing place,   and he has made   me glad.

2. I heard the voice of Jesus say,
   'Behold, I freely give
   the living water, thirsty one;
   stoop down and drink and live.'
   I came to Jesus, and I drank
   of that life-giving stream;
   my thirst was quenched, my soul revived,
   and now I live in him.

3. I heard the voice of Jesus say,
   'I am this dark world's light;
   look unto me, thy morn shall rise,
   and all thy day be bright.'
   I looked to Jesus, and I found
   in him my star, my sun;
   and in that light of life I'll walk
   till travelling days are done.

16 I met you at the cross

Words: Eric A. Thorn

Music: Roger Jones arr. Ann Routley from 'Tell me the stories of Jesus'

AT THE CROSS   64 64

Adagio (♩ = 70)

1. I met you at the cross, Je - sus, my Lord; I heard you from that cross; my name you called – asked me to fol-low you all of my days,

2. I saw you on the cross
   dying for me;
   I put you on that cross;
   but your one plea –
   would I now follow you all of my days,
   and would I evermore your great name praise?

3. Jesus, my Lord and King,
   Saviour of all;
   Jesus, the King of kings,
   you heard my call –
   that I would follow you all of my days,
   and that for evermore your name I'd praise.

17 Immortal, invisible, God only wise

Words: Walter Chalmers Smith (1824-1908)
Music: Roger Jones arr. Ann Routley from 'Ways to Praise'

IMMORTAL INVISIBLE   11 11 11 11

Moderato (♩ = 100)

name   we   praise.   2. Un -

2. Unresting, unhasting, and silent as light,
   nor wanting, nor wasting, thou rulest in might;
   thy justice like mountains high soaring above
   thy clouds which are fountains of goodness and love.

3. To all life thou givest, to both great and small;
   in all life thou livest, the true life of all;
   we blossom and flourish as leaves on the tree,
   and wither and perish; but nought changeth thee.

4. Great Father of glory, pure Father of light,
   thine angels adore thee, all veiling their sight;
   all laud we would render, O help us to see
   'tis only the splendour of light hideth thee.

18 In heavenly love abiding

Words: Anna Laetitia Waring (1823-1910)
Music: Roger Jones from 'Ways to Praise'

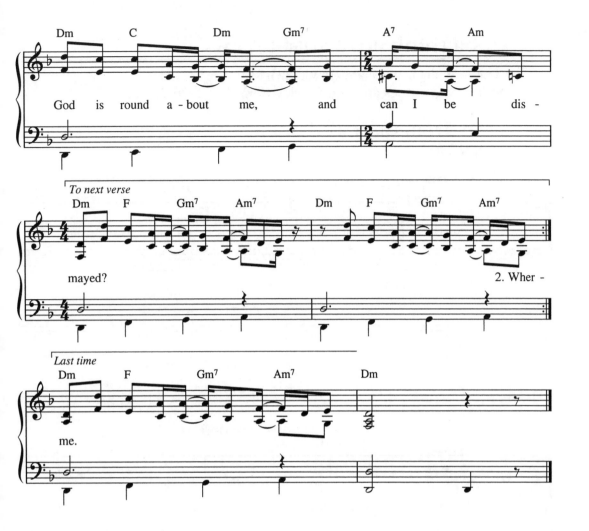

2. Wherever he may guide me,
   no want shall turn me back;
   my Shepherd is beside me,
   and nothing can I lack.
   His wisdom ever waketh,
   his sight is never dim,
   he knows the way he taketh,
   and I will walk with him.

3. Green pastures are before me,
   which yet I have not seen;
   bright skies will soon be o'er me,
   where the dark clouds have been.
   My hope I cannot measure,
   my path to life is free,
   my Saviour has my treasure,
   and he will walk with me.

19 It is a thing most wonderful

Words: William Walsham How (1823-1897)
Music: Roger Jones arr. Ann Routley from 'The Torn Curtain'

TORN CURTAIN 88 88 (LM)

Gently (♩ = 70)

1. It is a thing most won-der-ful, al-most too won-der-ful to be, that God's own Son should come from heav'n, and die to save a child like me.

2. And yet I know that it is true: he chose a poor and hum-ble lot, and wept and toiled, and mourned and died,

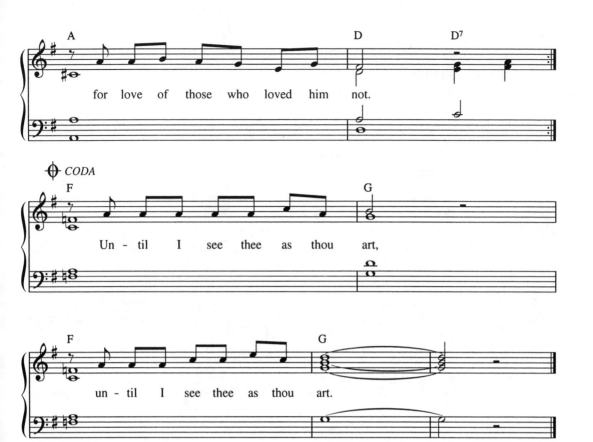

for love of those who loved him not.

CODA

Un - til I see thee as thou art,

un - til I see thee as thou art.

3. I cannot tell how he could love
   a child so weak and full of sin;
   his love must be most wonderful,
   if he could die my love to win.

4. I sometimes think about the cross,
   and close my eyes, and try to see
   the cruel nails and crown of thorns,
   and Jesus crucified for me.

5. But even could I see him die,
   I could but see a little part
   of that great love which, like a fire,
   is always burning in his heart.

6. It is most wonderful to know
   his love for me so free and sure;
   but 'tis more wonderful to see
   my love for him so faint and poor.

7. And yet I want to love thee, Lord;
   O light the flame within my heart,
   and I will love thee more and more,
   until I see thee as thou art.

20 Jesus, lover of my soul

Words: Charles Wesley (1707-1788)
Music: Roger Jones arr. Ann Routley from 'Pharisee'

ARIMATHEA 77 77 D

With life (♩ = 105)

1. Je-sus, lov-er of my soul, let me
to thy bo-som fly, while the near-er wa-ters roll,
while the tem-pest still is high: hide me,
O my Sa-viour, hide, till the storm of life is past;
safe in-to the ha-ven guide, O re-

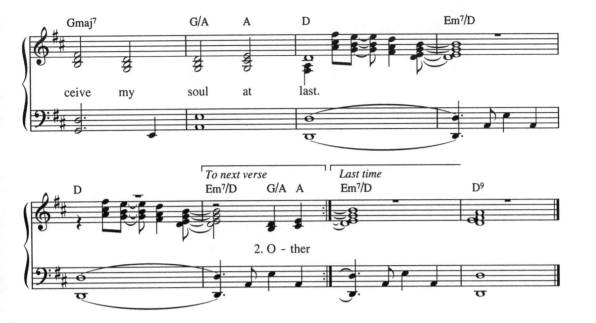

ceive my soul at last.

To next verse / Last time

2. O - ther

2. Other refuge have I none,
   hangs my helpless soul on thee;
   leave, ah, leave me not alone,
   still support and comfort me.
   All my trust on thee is stayed,
   all my help from thee I bring;
   cover my defenceless head
   with the shadow of thy wing.

3. Thou, O Christ, art all I want,
   more than all in thee I find;
   raise the fallen, cheer the faint,
   heal the sick and lead the blind.
   Just and holy is thy name,
   I am all unrighteousness;
   false and full of sin I am,
   thou art full of truth and grace.

4. Plenteous grace with thee is found,
   grace to cover all my sin;
   let the healing streams abound,
   make and keep me pure within.
   Thou of life the fountain art,
   freely let me take of thee;
   spring thou up within my heart,
   rise to all eternity.

21 Jesus shall reign where'er the sun

Words: Isaac Watts (1674-1748)
Music: Roger Jones from 'Precious and Honoured'

CHESTERFIELD 88 88 (LM)

2. To him shall endless prayer be made
and praises throng to crown his head;
his name, like sweet perfume, shall rise
with every morning sacrifice.

3. People and realms of every tongue
dwell on his love with sweetest song,
and infant voices shall proclaim
their early blessings on his name.

4. Blessings abound where'er he reigns:
the prisoner leaps to lose his chains;
the weary find eternal rest,
and all the sons of want are blest.

5. Let every creature rise and bring
peculiar honours to our King;
angels descend with songs again,
and earth repeat the loud 'Amen'.

22 Just as I am

Words: Charlotte Elliot (1789-1871)
Music: Roger Jones arr. Ann Routley from 'Ways to Praise'

I come. O Lamb of God, I come.

2. Just as I am, and waiting not
   to rid my soul of one dark blot,
   to thee, whose blood can cleanse each spot,
   O Lamb of God, I come.

3. Just as I am, though tossed about
   with many a conflict, many a doubt,
   fightings and fears within, without,
   O Lamb of God, I come.

4. Just as I am, poor, wretched, blind;
   sight, riches, healing of the mind,
   yea, all I need, in thee to find,
   O Lamb of God, I come.

5. Just as I am, thou wilt receive,
   wilt welcome, pardon, cleanse, relieve:
   because thy promise I believe,
   O Lamb of God, I come.

6. Just as I am, thy love unknown
   has broken every barrier down,
   now to be thine, yea, thine alone,
   O Lamb of God, I come.

7. Just as I am, of that free love
   the breadth, length, depth and height to prove,
   here for a season, then above,
   O Lamb of God, I come.

23 Lord, thy word abideth

Words: Henry Williams Baker (1821-1877)
Music: Roger Jones arr. Ann Routley from 'Greater Than Gold'

Lord, thy word a-bid - eth, and our foot-steps guid - eth; who its truth be-liev - eth light and joy re - ceiv - eth.

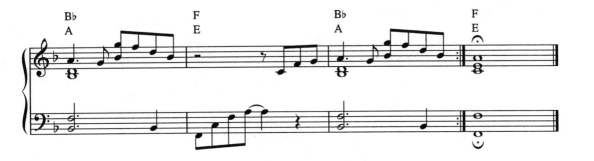

2. When our foes are near us,
   then thy word doth cheer us,
   word of consolation,
   message of salvation.

3. When the storms are o'er us,
   and dark clouds before us,
   then its light directeth
   and our way protecteth.

4. Who can tell the pleasure,
   who recount the treasure,
   by thy word imparted
   to the simple-hearted?

5. Word of mercy, giving
   succour to the living;
   word of life, supplying
   comfort to the dying.

6. O that we, discerning
   its most holy learning,
   Lord, may love and fear thee,
   evermore be near thee.

24 Man of sorrows!

Words: Philip Bliss (1838-1876)

Music: Roger Jones arr. Ann Routley from 'From Pharaoh to Freedom'

BURNEY LANE 77 78

Adagio con espressione ($\quad$ = 60)

Unaccompanied SATB parts for verse 3

2. Bearing shame and scoffing rude,
   in my place condemned he stood;
   sealed my pardon with his blood;
   Hallelujah! What a Saviour!

3. Guilty, vile and helpless we;
   spotless Lamb of God was he:
   full atonement – can it be?
   Hallelujah! What a Saviour!

4. Lifted up was he to die:
   'It is finished!' was his cry;
   Now in heaven exalted high;
   Hallelujah! What a Saviour!

5. When he comes, our glorious King,
   all his ransomed home to bring,
   then anew this song we'll sing:
   Hallelujah! Hallelujah!
   Hallelujah! What a Saviour!

25 May the mind of Christ

Words: Kate B. Wilkinson (1859-1928)
Music: Roger Jones

MIND OF CHRIST   87 85
Relaxed (♩ = 90)

1. May the mind of Christ my Sa - viour
live in me from day to day, by his love and pow'r
con - trol - ling all I do and say.

2. May the word of God dwell rich - ly in my heart from hour
to hour, so that all may see
me tri - umph on - ly through his pow'r.

3. May the peace of God my Father
   rule my life in everything,
   that I may be calm to comfort
   sick and sorrowing.

4. May the love of Jesus fill me,
   as the waters fill the sea;
   him exalting, self abasing,
   this is victory.

5. May I run the race before me,
   strong and brave to face the foe,
   looking only unto Jesus,
   as I onward go.

26 My God, how wonderful thou art

Words: Frederick William Faber (1814-1863)
Music: Roger Jones arr. Ann Routley from 'Ways to praise'

by pros-trate spi - rits day and night in-ces-sant-ly a - dored, in-ces-sant-

ly a-dored! My My God, how won-der - ful thou art!

2. How wonderful, how beautiful,
   the sight of thee must be,
   thine endless wisdom, boundless power,
   and awesome purity, and awesome purity!

3. O how I fear thee, living God,
   with deepest, tenderest fears,
   and worship thee with trembling hope,
   and penitential tears, and penitential tears!

4. Yet may I love thee too, O Lord,
   almighty as thou art,
   for thou hast stooped to ask of me
   the love of my poor heart, the love of my poor heart!

5. No earthly father loves like thee,
   no mother, e'er so mild,
   bears and forbears as thou hast done
   with me thy sinful child, with me thy sinful child!

6. Father of Jesus, love's reward,
   what rapture will it be,
   prostrate before thy throne to lie,
   and gaze and gaze on thee, and gaze and gaze on thee!

27 My hope is built

Words: I. Mote (1797-1874)
Music: Roger Jones from 'Precious and Honoured'

ROCK SOLID   88 88 88 extended
Rock style (♩ = 140)

1. My hope is built on no-thing less than Je-sus' blood and right-eous-ness; no mer-it of my own I claim, but whol-ly trust in Je - sus' name.

Refrain

On Christ, the sol - id rock, I stand – all o-ther ground is sink-ing sand! On Christ, the sol - id

rock, I stand – all o-ther ground is sink - ing

sand!

2. When weary in this earthly race,
   I rest on his unchanging grace;
   in every wild and stormy gale
   my anchor holds and will not fail.

3. His vow, his covenant and blood
   are my defence against the flood;
   when earthly hopes are swept away
   he will uphold me on that day.

4. When the last trumpet's voice shall sound,
   O may I then in him be found!
   Clothed in his righteousness alone,
   faultless to stand before his throne.

28 My Jesus, I love thee

Words: William Featherstone
Music: Roger Jones arr. Ann Routley

MY JESUS   11 11 11 11
Simply, with intimacy (♩ = 105)

1. My Je - sus, I love thee, I know thou art mine; for thee all the fol - lies of sin I re - sign. My gra - cious Re - deem - er, my Sa - viour art thou;

if e - ver I loved thee, my Je - sus, 'tis now.

2. I

2. I love thee, because thou hast first loved me,
   and purchased my pardon on Calvary's tree;
   I love thee for wearing the thorns on thy brow;
   if ever I loved thee, my Jesus, 'tis now.

3. I'll love thee in life, I will love thee in death,
   and praise thee as long as thou lendest me breath;
   and say when the death-dew lies cold on my brow;
   if ever I loved thee, my Jesus, 'tis now.

4. In mansions of glory and endless delight,
   I'll ever adore thee in heaven so bright;
   I'll sing with the glittering crown on my brow;
   if ever I loved thee, my Jesus, 'tis now.

29 New every morning

Words: John Keble (1792-1886)
Music: Roger Jones arr. Ann Routley

LAUNDE 88 88 (LM)
Unhurried (♩ = 60)

1. New ev – 'ry morn-ing is the love
our wak –ing and up – ris – ing prove;
through sleep and dark – ness safe-ly brought,
re-stored to life
and pow'r and thought.

2. New mercies, each returning day,
   surround your people as they pray;
   new dangers past, new sins forgiven,
   new thoughts of God, new hopes of heaven.

3. If in our daily life our mind
   be set to hallow all we find,
   new treasures still, of countless price,
   God will provide for sacrifice.

4. The trivial round, the common task,
   will give us all we ought to ask,
   room to deny ourselves, a road
   to bring us daily nearer God.

5. Prepare us, Lord, in your dear love
   for perfect rest with you above;
   and help us, this and every day,
   to grow more like you as we pray.

30 Now thank we all our God

Words: Martin Rinckart (1586-1649) trans. Catherine Winkworth (1829-1878)
Music: Roger Jones

way   with   count - less   gifts   of   love,   and   still   is

ours   to - day.   2. O   - more.

2. O may this bounteous God
   through all our life be near us,
   with ever joyful hearts
   and blessed peace to cheer us;
   and keep us in his grace,
   and guide us when perplexed,
   and free us from all ills
   in this world and the next.

3. All praise and thanks to God
   the Father now be given,
   the Son and him who reigns
   with them in highest heaven,
   the one eternal God,
   whom earth and heaven adore;
   for thus it was, is now,
   and shall be evermore.

31 O Jesus, I have promised

Words: J.E. Bode (1816-1874)
Music: Roger Jones arr. Ann Routley from 'Ways to Praise'

2. O let me feel thee near me:
   the world is ever near;
   I see the sights that dazzle,
   the tempting sounds I hear;
   my foes are ever near me,
   around me and within;
   but Jesus, draw thou nearer,
   and shield my soul from sin.

3. O let me hear thee speaking
   in accents clear and still,
   above the storms of passion,
   the murmurs of self-will;
   O speak to reassure me,
   to hasten or control;
   O speak and make me listen,
   thou guardian of my soul.

4. O Jesus, thou hast promised
   to all who follow thee,
   that where thou art in glory
   there shall thy servants be;
   and, Jesus, I have promised
   to serve thee to the end:
   O give me grace to follow,
   my Master and my friend.

5. O let me see thy foot-marks
   and in them plant my own;
   my hope to follow duly
   is in thy strength alone.
   O guide me, call me, draw me,
   uphold me to the end;
   and then in heaven receive me,
   my Saviour and my friend.

32 O love that will not let me go

Words: George Matheson (1842-1906)
Music: Roger Jones arr. Ann Routley from 'Angel Voices'

2. O Light that followest all my way,
   I yield my flickering torch to thee;
   my heart restores its borrowed ray,
   that in thy sunshine's blaze its day
   may brighter, fairer be.

4. O Cross that liftest up my head,
   I dare not ask to fly from thee:
   I lay in dust life's glory dead,
   and from the ground there blossoms red
   life that shall endless be.

Harmony parts for verse 3

33 O thou, who camest from above

Words: Charles Wesley (1707-1788)
Music: Roger Jones from 'Precious and Honoured'

NEWTHORPE   88 88   (LM)

With warmth (♩ = 120)

2. There let it for thy glory burn
   with inextinguishable blaze,
   and, trembling, to its source return
   in humble love and fervent praise.

3. Jesus, confirm my heart's desire
   to work and speak and think for thee;
   still let me guard thy holy fire
   and still stir up thy gift in me.

4. Ready for all thy perfect will,
   my acts of faith and love repeat,
   till death thine endless mercies seal,
   and make the sacrifice complete.

34 Praise to the holiest in the height

Words: John Henry Newman (1801-1890)
Music: Roger Jones arr. Ann Routley from 'Snakes and Ladders'

EDGBASTON   86 86 (CM)

Energetically ($\downarrow$ = 125)

Praise to the ho-liest in the height,

and in the depth be praise;

in all his words most won-der - ful, most

sure in all his ways.

Last time to Coda (Overleaf)

Harmony parts for SATB will be found overleaf

2. O wisest love! that flesh and blood,
   which did in Adam fail,
   should strive afresh against their foe,
   should strive and should prevail;

3. And that a higher gift than grace
   should flesh and blood refine,
   God's presence and his very self,
   and essence all-divine.

4. O generous love! that he who smote
   in Man for man the foe,
   the double agony in Man
   for man should undergo;

5. And in the garden secretly,
   and on the cross on high,
   should teach his brethren, and inspire
   to suffer and to die.

   Refrain twice after verse 5

35 Saviour, again to thy dear name we raise

Words: John Ellerton (1826-1893)
Music: Roger Jones arr. Ann Routley from 'Precious and Honoured'

HENLEY-IN-ARDEN 10 10 10 10

Reverently (♩ = 100)

1. Sa - viour, a - gain to thy dear name we raise

with one ac - cord our part - ing hymn of praise;

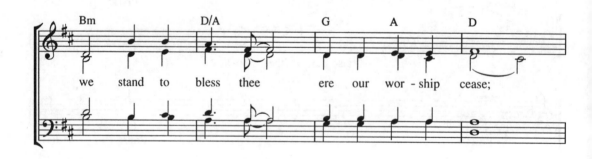

we stand to bless thee ere our wor - ship cease;

then, low - ly kneel - ing, wait thy word of peace.

2. Grant us thy peace upon our homeward way;
   with thee began, with thee shall end the day:
   guard thou the lips from sin, the hearts from shame,
   that in this house have called upon thy name.

3. Grant us thy peace, Lord, through the coming night;
   turn thou for us its darkness into light;
   from harm and danger keep thy children free,
   for dark and light are both alike to thee.

4. Grant us thy peace throughout our earthly life,
   our balm in sorrow, and our stay in strife;
   then, when thy voice shall bid our conflict cease,
   call us, O Lord, to thine eternal peace.

36 Spirit divine

Words: A. Reed (1787-1862)
Music: Roger Jones from 'Ways to Praise'

CODA

and lead us in those paths of life where all the right-eous go.

come, great

Spi - rit, come!

3. Come as the fire, and purge our hearts
   like sacrificial flame;
   let our whole soul an offering be
   to our Redeemer's name.

4. Come as the dew, and sweetly bless
   this consecrated hour;
   may barrenness rejoice to own
   thy fertilizing power.

5. Come as the dove, and spread thy wings,
   the wings of peaceful love;
   and let thy Church on earth become
   blest as the Church above.

6. Come as the wind, with rushing sound
   and Pentecostal grace;
   that all of woman born may see
   the glory of thy face.

7. Spirit divine, attend our prayers,
   make a lost world thy home;
   descend with all thy gracious powers;
   O come, great Spirit, come!

37 Take my life, and let it be

Words: Francis Ridley Havergal (1836-1879)
Music: Roger Jones

TAKE MY LIFE   77 77

Moderato

1. Take my life, and let it be con-se-crat-ed, Lord, to thee; take my mo - ments and my days, let them flow in cease-less praise, let them flow in cease-less praise.

2. Take my hands, and let them move
   at the impulse of thy love;
   take my feet, and let them be
   swift and beautiful for thee,
   swift and beautiful for thee.

3. Take my voice, and let me sing
   always, only, for my King;
   take my lips, and let them be
   filled with messages from thee,
   filled with messages from thee.

4. Take my silver and my gold;
   not a mite would I withhold;
   take my intellect, and use
   ev'ry power as thou shalt choose,
   ev'ry power as thou shalt choose.

5. Take my will, and make it thine:
   it shall be no longer mine;
   take my heart: it is thine own;
   it shall be thy royal throne,
   it shall be thy royal throne.

6. Take my love; my Lord, I pour
   at thy feet its treasure-store;
   take myself, and I will be
   ever, only, all for thee,
   ever, only, all for thee.

38 Tell me the stories of Jesus

Words: W.H. Parker (1845-1929) alt.
Music: Roger Jones arr. Ann Routley from 'Greater Than Gold'

STORIES OF JESUS   84 84 54 54

2. First let me hear how the children stood round his knee
   and I shall fancy his blessing resting on me;
   words full of kindness, deeds full of grace,
   all in the lovelight of Jesus' face.

3. Into the city I'd follow the children's band,
   waving a branch of the palm tree high in my hand;
   one of his heralds, yes, I would sing
   loudest hosannas: 'Jesus is King!'

4. Show me that scene in the garden of bitter pain,
   and of the cross where my Saviour for me was slain;
   and through the sadness, help me to see
   how Jesus suffered for love of me.

5. Gladly I'd hear of his rising out of the grave,
   living and strong and triumphant, mighty to save;
   and how he sends us all men to bring
   stories of Jesus, Jesus their King.

6. *Repeat verse 1*

39 There is a green hill far away

Words: Cecil Frances Alexander (1818-1895)
Music: Roger Jones arr. Ann Routley from 'Mary Magdalene'

MAGDALENE 86 86 (CM)

Andante (♩ = 75)

1. There is a green hill far a - way, with - out a ci - ty wall, where the dear Lord was cru - ci - fied who died to save us all. 2. We may not know, we can - not tell, what pains he had to

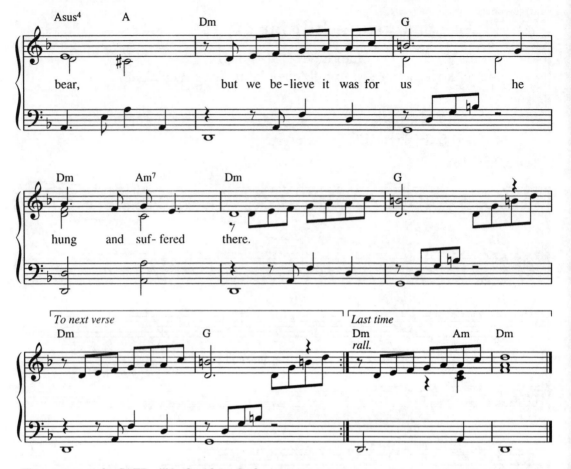

Harmony parts for SATB will be found overleaf

3. He died that we might be forgiven,
   he died to make us good;
   that we might go at last to heaven,
   saved by his precious blood.

4. There was no other good enough
   to pay the price of sin;
   he only could unlock the gate
   of heaven, and let us in.

5. O, dearly, dearly has he loved,
   and we must love him too,
   and trust in his redeeming blood,
   and try his works to do.

   Repeat verse 5

Harmony parts for SATB

1. There is a green hill far a - way, with - out a ci - ty wall, where the dear Lord was cru - ci - fied who died to save us all.

2. We may not know, we can - not tell, what pains he had to bear, but we be - lieve it was for us he hung and suf - fered there.

3. He died that we might be forgiven,
he died to make us good;
that we might go at last to heaven,
saved by his precious blood.

4. There was no other good enough
to pay the price of sin;
he only could unlock the gate
of heaven, and let us in.

5. O, dearly, dearly has he loved,
and we must love him too,
and trust in his redeeming blood,
and try his works to do.

Repeat verse 5

40 What a friend we have in Jesus

Words: Joseph Scriven (1819-1886)
Music: Roger Jones from 'Ways to Praise'

2. Have we trials and temptations?
   Is there trouble anywhere?
   we should never be discouraged:
   take it to the Lord in prayer!
   Can we find a friend so faithful,
   who will all our sorrows share?
   Jesus knows our every weakness –
   take it to the Lord in prayer!

3. Are we weak and heavy-laden,
   cumbered with a load of care?
   Precious Saviour, still our refuge,
   take it to the Lord in prayer!
   Do thy friends despise, forsake thee?
   Take it to the Lord in prayer!
   In his arms he'll take and shield thee,
   thou wilt find a solace there.

41 When I survey the wondrous cross

Words: Isaac Watts (1674-1748)
Music: Roger Jones arr. Ann Routley from 'Saints Alive'

pour con-tempt on all my pride.

2. Forbid it, Lord, that I should boast,
   save in the death of Christ, my God:
   all the vain things that charm me most,
   I sacrifice them to his blood,
   I sacrifice them to his blood.

3. See from his head, his hands, his feet,
   sorrow and love flow mingling down:
   did e'er such love and sorrow meet,
   or thorns compose so rich a crown,
   or thorns compose so rich a crown?

4. Were the whole realm of nature mine,
   that were an offering far too small;
   love so amazing, so divine,
   demands my soul, my life, my all,
   demands my soul, my life, my all.